Let's Talk Maths

for ages 7–9

Andrew Brodie ✔

Contents

This series of three books, will help every school in the delivery of 'a renewed focus on oral and mental mathematics' as recommended in the Rose Review and the Williams Review of Mathematics Teaching.

The Rose Review of the primary curriculum (April 2009) recommends:

Primary schools should make sure that children's spoken communication is developed intensively within all subjects and for learning across the curriculum.

The Review of Mathematics Teaching states that the existing curriculum for mathematics is well balanced and should continue in its current form but it adds:

Two issues only are singled out: the need for an increased focus on the 'use and application' of mathematics and on the vitally important question of the classroom discussion of mathematics. It is often suggested that 'mathematics itself is a language' but it must not be overlooked that only by constructive dialogue in the medium of the English language in the classroom can logic and reasoning be fully developed – the factors at the very heart of embedded learning in mathematics.

In considering pedagogy the Review notes:

It must be truly interactive, giving children time, for example, to think, to question as well as answer, to discuss and to try out their own ideas and strategies.

The critical importance of engaging children in discussing mathematics is widely recognised. This, of course, includes learning and using mathematical language. Talking mathematics should not be seen simply as a rehearsal in class of the vocabulary of mathematics, novel and important though that may be for the young learner. It should extend to high quality discussion that develops children's logic, reasoning and deduction skills, and underpins all mathematical learning activity. The ultimate goal is to develop mathematical understanding – comprehension of mathematical ideas and applications.

How to use this book

Let's Talk Maths provides opportunities for teachers to use, and reuse, stimulating whiteboard displays that encourage pupils to discuss mathematics using appropriate mathematical vocabulary.

Each double-page spread in the teachers' notes features detailed instructions, including questions to prompt discussion, on how to use the CD content and a screenshot of the typical view that the children will see on the interactive whiteboard. The teachers' notes specify the prior learning that the children need, together with learning objectives and success criteria. The notes also give an indication for which Blocks the activity is suitable.

How to use the CD

Choose an activity from the main menu:

Activity navigation:

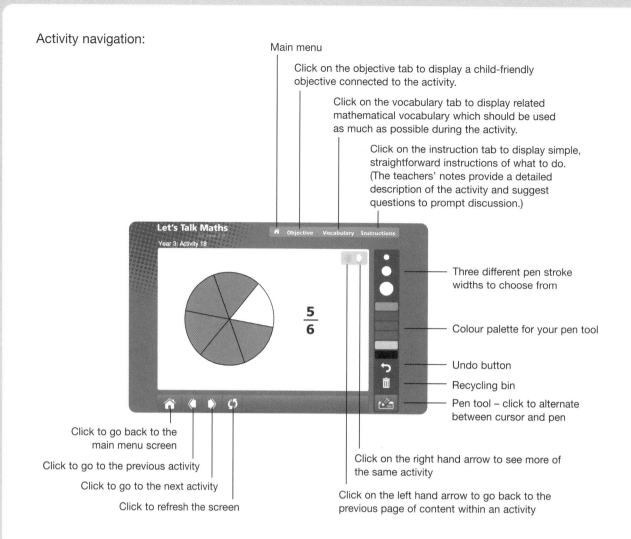

Main menu

Click on the objective tab to display a child-friendly objective connected to the activity.

Click on the vocabulary tab to display related mathematical vocabulary which should be used as much as possible during the activity.

Click on the instruction tab to display simple, straightforward instructions of what to do. (The teachers' notes provide a detailed description of the activity and suggest questions to prompt discussion.)

Three different pen stroke widths to choose from

Colour palette for your pen tool

Undo button

Recycling bin

Pen tool – click to alternate between cursor and pen

Click to go back to the main menu screen

Click to go to the previous activity

Click to go to the next activity

Click to refresh the screen

Click on the right hand arrow to see more of the same activity

Click on the left hand arrow to go back to the previous page of content within an activity

Speaking and Listening in Key Stage 2

This is the second book in the series and is designed to be used with children in Years 3 and 4. As you will have read on page 3, he importance of encouraging children to listen carefully and to speak appropriately in all aspects of the curriculum is reflected in national guidance for the teaching of mathematics. Opportunities are found for engaging pupils in speaking and listening activities in each unit of the teaching blocks specified in the Guidance for Planning for Year 3 and Year 4. Suggestions for incorporating most of the learning objectives for 'Speaking', 'Listening and responding' and 'Group discussion and interaction' specified in the Primary Framework for Literacy are linked to specific units for mathematics:

Year 3 Speaking

■ Explain a process or present information, ensuring that items are clearly sequenced, relevant details are included and accounts are ended effectively
   Block A Unit 1, Block C Unit 3, Block D Units 1, 2 and 3

■ Sustain conversation, explain or give reasons for their views or choices
   Block B Units 1 and 2, Block E Units 1 and 2

■ Develop and use specific vocabulary in different contexts
   Block B Unit 3, Block E Unit 3

Year 3 Listening and responding

■ Follow up others' points and show whether they agree or disagree in a whole class discussion
Block A Unit 2

■ Identify the presentational features used to communicate the main points
Block C Unit 2

Year 3 Group discussion and interaction

■ Actively include and respond to all members of the group
Block A Unit 3

■ Use talk to organise roles and action
Block C Unit 1

Year 4 Speaking

■ Use and reflect on some ground rules for dialogue (eg making structured, extended contributions, speaking audibly, making meaning explicit and listening actively) - note that this wording is different to that which appears in the framework for literacy
Block A Unit 1

■ Respond appropriately to the contributions of others in the light of alternative viewpoints
Block A Unit 2, Block E Unit 1

Year 4 Listening and responding

■ Listen to a speaker and make notes on the talk
Block B Unit 1, Block D Unit 1

■ Investigate how talk varies with age, familiarity, gender and purpose
Block B Unit 2

Year 4 Group discussion and interaction

■ Take different roles in groups and use the language appropriate to them, including the roles of leader, reporter, scribe and mentor
Block D Units 2 and 3

■ Use time, resources and group members efficiently by distributing tasks, checking progress and making back-up plans
Block B Unit 3, Block C Units 1, 2 and 3, Block E Unit 3

■ Identify the main points of each speaker, compare their arguments and how they are presented
Block A Unit 3, Block E Unit 2

Read and order whole numbers to at least 1000

Building on previous learning

Before starting this unit check that the children can already:

☐ read and write two-digit and three-digit numbers in figures and words

Learning objectives

- Read numerals from 0 to 1000
- Use knowledge of place value to position these numbers on a number line
- Count on from and back to zero in single-digit steps or multiples of 10

Learning outcomes

The children will be able to:

- read two-digit and three-digit numbers in figures
- relate all these to the number line
- use appropriate vocabulary
- talk confidently about the numbers
- count on from and back to zero in single-digit steps or multiples of 10

Success criteria

Can the children…

☐ read confidently the numbers pointed out to them?

☐ arrange the numbers in order from smallest to biggest or from biggest to smallest?

☐ count on from and back to zero in single-digit steps?

☐ count on from and back to zero in multiples of 10?

☐ listen and talk confidently using some of the vocabulary listed and some of the question types shown?

How to use the material for discussion

The adult should start with asking questions to provide a structure but should try to withdraw from the discussion and allow the children to take over so that they are asking questions of each other. They will, at times, need to be reminded of the appropriate vocabulary and you may wish to encourage them to use the vocabulary listed.

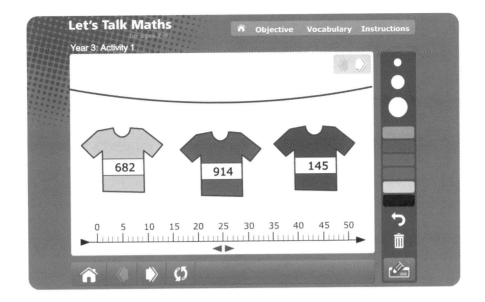

The activity could open with questions of the following type:

● What is this number? Can you read this number?
● How many digits does this number have?

If you feel that the children are confident, different questions can be used:

● What number is one more than this number?
● What number is one less than this number?
● What number is ten more than this number?
● What number is ten less than this number?
● What number is one hundred more than this number?
● What number is one hundred less than this number?
● Can you count up from this number in tens?

Now ask which number should be first if we wish to put them in order starting with the smallest. Ask another child which number should come next. Ensure that the children discuss the place value of the digits and that they realise that the hundreds digit will be the most important one to consider first. When all the numbers have been put in order from smallest to biggest, ask a child to be the leader with a new set of numbers.

Appropriate vocabulary

show me	read	count
count to	count on	count on to
count on from	count up to	count up from
compare	order	more
less	biggest	smallest
before	after	zero, one, two, three, etc.
explain	digit	pattern
place value	ones	tens
hundreds	thousand	one-digit number
two-digit number	three-digit number	four-digit number

Partition three-digit numbers into multiples of 100, 10 and 1

Building on previous learning

Before starting this unit check that the children can already:

- [ ] read and write two-digit and three-digit numbers
- [ ] read numerals from 0 to 1000

Learning objectives

- Partition three-digit numbers into multiples of 100, 10 and 1. (Note that Year 3 Activity 2 encourages children to observe how three-digit numbers can be seen to constitute hundreds, tens and ones – this understanding leads to the ability to partition.)

Learning outcomes

The children will be able to:

- read two-digit and three-digit numbers in figures
- relate all these to the number line
- use appropriate vocabulary
- talk confidently about the numbers
- 'build' three-digit numbers by combining hundreds, tens and ones

Success criteria

Can the children…

- [ ] build specified three-digit numbers?
- [ ] listen and talk confidently using some of the vocabulary listed and some of the question types shown?

How to use the material for discussion

The adult should start with asking questions to provide a structure but should try to withdraw from the discussion and allow the children to take over so that they are asking questions of each other. They will, at times, need to be reminded of the appropriate vocabulary and you may wish to encourage them to use the vocabulary listed.

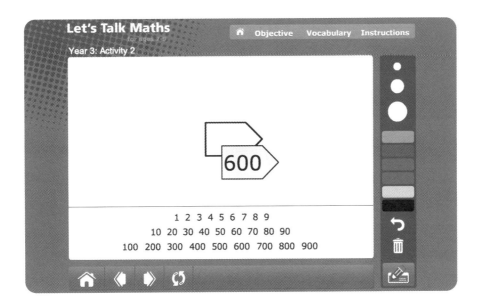

The activity consists of the teacher, or a pupil playing the role of leader, asking pupils to build a specified three-digit number, eg:

- Can you make the number 547?

A pupil then comes to the screen and drags the appropriate numbers from the number bank at the bottom of the screen to the place value box where the numbers merge to make the number specified.

A further feature of the activity is that the constituent parts of the number can be taken away. For example, ask the child to take away 40 from 547 – if s/he drags the 40 away the 507 will remain in the centre box.

Appropriate vocabulary

show me	read	count
zero, one, two, three, etc.	pattern	take away
'teens' number	explain	digit
place value	ones	tens
hundreds	thousand	one-digit number
two-digit number	three-digit number	

Round two-digit numbers to the nearest 10

Building on previous learning

Before starting this unit check that the children can already:

☐ read and write two-digit and three-digit numbers

☐ read numerals from 0 to 1000

☐ recognise multiples of 5 and 10

Learning objectives

■ Round two-digit numbers to the nearest 10

Learning outcomes

The children will be able to:

■ round up or down to the nearest multiple of 10

■ round up to the nearest 10 from a multiple of 5

Success criteria

Can the children...

☐ match two-digit numbers to the appropriate positions on a number line?

☐ round two-digit numbers up or down to the nearest multiple of 10

☐ round up to the nearest 10 from a multiple of 5

☐ listen and talk confidently using some of the vocabulary listed?

How to use the material for discussion

Children will find the displayed number on the number line and then round it up to the nearest 10. As with all of the activities the teacher can start the discussion using appropriate vocabulary and questions but should then encourage the pupils to take turns in leading the discussion.

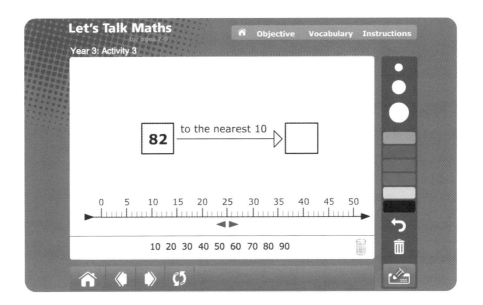

The activity consists of the teacher, or a pupil playing the role of leader, asking pupils to round a two-digit number to the nearest 10. The children can discuss to which multiple of 10 the number displayed in the left hand box is closest to. (Numbers that are multiples of 5 will provide opportunities to discuss the rule of rounding up.) The child can then drag the appropriate multiple of ten from the bottom of the screen to the right hand box. When the child clicks on the left hand box a new two-digit number will be displayed.

Appropriate vocabulary

show me	read	explain
pattern	place value	digit
ones	tens	one-digit number
two-digit number	compare	order
round	nearest	approximate
estimate		

Round three-digit numbers to the nearest 100

Building on previous learning

Before starting this unit check that the children can already:

- [ ] read and write two-digit and three-digit numbers
- [ ] read numerals from 0 to 1000
- [ ] recognise multiples of 5 and 10

Learning objectives

- Round three-digit numbers to the nearest 100

Learning outcomes

The children will be able to:

- round up or down to the nearest multiple of 100
- round up to the nearest 100 from a multiple of 50

Success criteria

Can the children…

- [ ] match three-digit numbers to the appropriate positions on a number line?
- [ ] round three-digit numbers up or down to the nearest multiple of 100?
- [ ] round up to the nearest 100 from a multiple of 50?
- [ ] listen and talk confidently using some of the vocabulary listed?

How to use the material for discussion

Children will find the displayed number on the number line and then round it up to the nearest multiple of 100. As with all of the activities the teacher can start the discussion using appropriate vocabulary and questions but should then encourage the pupils to take turns in leading the discussion.

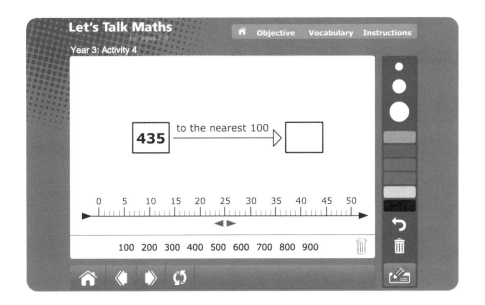

The activity consists of the teacher, or a pupil playing the role of leader, asking pupils to round a three-digit number to the nearest 100. The children can discuss to which multiple of 100 the number in the left hand box is closest to. (Numbers that are multiples of 50 will provide opportunities to discuss the rule of rounding up.) The child can then drag the appropriate multiple of 100 from the bottom of the screen to the right hand box. When the child clicks on the left hand box a new three-digit number will be displayed.

Appropriate vocabulary

show me	read	explain
pattern	place value	digit
ones	tens	hundreds
one-digit number	two-digit number	three-digit number
compare	order	round
nearest	approximate	estimate

Round three-digit numbers to the nearest 10 or 100

Building on previous learning

Before starting this unit check that the children can already:

- [ ] read and write two-digit and three-digit numbers
- [ ] read numerals from 0 to 1000
- [ ] recognise multiples of 5 and 10
- [ ] round two-digit numbers to the nearest 10
- [ ] round three-digit numbers to the nearest 100

Learning objectives

- Round three-digit numbers to the nearest 100 or 10

Learning outcomes

The children will be able to:

- round three-digit numbers up or down to the nearest multiple of 100
- round up to the nearest 100 from a multiple of 50
- round three-digit numbers up or down to the nearest multiple of 10
- round up to the nearest 10 from a multiple of 5

Success criteria

Can the children…

- [ ] match three-digit numbers to the appropriate positions on a number line?
- [ ] round three-digit numbers up or down to the nearest multiple of 100?
- [ ] round up to the nearest 100 from a multiple of 50?
- [ ] round three-digit numbers up or down to the nearest multiple of 10?
- [ ] listen and talk confidently using some of the vocabulary listed?

How to use the material for discussion

This activity should be used with the pupils once they are confident with Activity 3 and Activity 4. Children will find the displayed number on the number line and then round it up to the nearest multiple of 100. Many children will find the next step more difficult – matching the three-digit number to the nearest multiple of 10.
As with all of the activities the teacher can start the discussion using appropriate vocabulary and questions but should then encourage the pupils to take turns in leading the discussion.

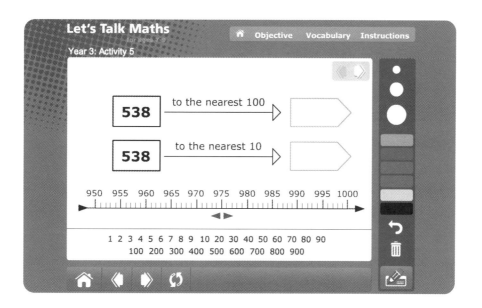

The activity consists of the teacher, or a pupil playing the role of leader, asking pupils to round a three-digit number to the nearest 100 and to the nearest 10. The children can first discuss to which multiple of 100 or 10 it is closest. A child can then drag the appropriate multiple of 100 and the appropriate multiple of 10 from the bank at the bottom of the screen into the place value boxes. When the top right hand arrow is clicked a new three-digit number will be displayed.

Appropriate vocabulary

show me	read	explain
pattern	place value	digit
ones	tens	hundreds
one-digit number	two-digit number	three-digit number
compare	order	round
nearest	approximate	estimate

Year 3 Activity 6

Derive and recall all addition facts for each number to 20

Building on previous learning

Before starting this unit check that the children can already:

☐ derive and recall all addition and subtraction facts for each number to at least 10

☐ calculate the value of an unknown in a number sentence

Learning objectives

■ Derive all addition facts for each number to 20

Learning outcomes

The children will be able to:

■ derive all addition facts for each number to 20

■ recall all addition facts for each number to 20

Success criteria

Can the children...

☐ create appropriate addition sentences for each randomly produced number?

☐ derive the addition facts for each number to 20?

☐ remember the addition facts for each number to 20?

☐ listen and talk confidently using some of the vocabulary listed?

How to use the material for discussion

The children's task is to create addition sentences with a total of the number shown. As with all of the activities the teacher can start the discussion using appropriate vocabulary and questions but should then encourage the pupils to take turns in leading the discussion. Encourage the children to produce several addition sentences for each number then to click the top right hand arrow to display a new target number. This activity can be repeated regularly and would be very useful as a lesson starter.

Let's Talk Maths
for ages
Year 3: Activity 6

Objective　Vocabulary　Instructions

17				
12	+		=	17
	+	15	=	17
16	+	1	=	
17		0	=	17

0 1 2 3 4 5 6 7 8 9 10 11 12 13 14 15 16 17 18 19 20 − + =

The activity consists of the teacher, or a pupil playing the role of leader, asking pupils to create addition sentences to match a target number. When the child clicks on the top right hand arrow a new number will be displayed. The leader asks one of the other pupils for a number to start an addition number sentence – they will soon realise that this first number must be less than or equal to the focus number. They can collect this number from the number bank then insert the addition sign and ask another pupil for the number that will make the total of the target number. They should complete the addition sentence with the equals sign and a copy of the target number.

Now another child could take the role of leader. Once several number sentences have been created for the target number, the screen can be cleared and a new target number can be displayed by clicking on the top right hand arrow.

Appropriate vocabulary

sign	symbol	addition
one-digit number	two-digit number	equals
addition sentence	number sentence	ones
tens	count on	add
sum	total	plus

Derive and recall all subtraction facts for each number to 20

Building on previous learning

Before starting this unit check that the children can already:

☐ derive and recall all addition and subtraction facts for each number to at least 10

☐ calculate the value of an unknown in a number sentence

Learning objectives

■ Derive all subtraction facts for each number to 20

Learning outcomes

The children will be able to:

■ derive all subtraction facts for each number to 20

■ recall all subtraction facts for each number to 20

Success criteria

Can the children…

☐ create appropriate subtraction sentences for each randomly produced number?

☐ derive the subtraction facts for each number to 20?

☐ remember the subtraction facts for each number to 20?

☐ listen and talk confidently using some of the vocabulary listed?

How to use the material for discussion

The children's task is to create subtraction sentences. As with all of the activities the teacher can start the discussion using appropriate vocabulary and questions but should then encourage the pupils to take turns in leading the discussion. Encourage the children to produce several subtraction sentences for each number. This activity can be repeated regularly and would be very useful as a lesson starter.

Let's Talk Maths
for ages 7-8

Year 3: Activity 7

14				
14	−		=	9
	−	7	=	7
14	−	0	=	
14	−		=	3

0 1 2 3 4 5 6 7 8 9 10 11 12 13 14 15 16 17 18 19 20 − + =

Objective   Vocabulary   Instructions

The activity consists of the teacher, or a pupil playing the role of leader, asking pupils to create subtraction sentences to match a target number. The leader asks one of the other pupils for a number to start a subtraction number sentence – they will soon realise that this first number must be the same as the target number. They can collect this number from the number bank then insert the subtraction sign and ask another pupil for a number to subtract from the target number. They should then ask another child to complete the subtraction sentence with the equals sign and the answer.

Now another child could take the role of leader. Once several number sentences have been created for the target number, a new target number can be displayed by clicking the top right hand arrow.

Appropriate vocabulary

sign	symbol	subtraction
one-digit number	two-digit number	equals
subtraction sentence	number sentence	ones
tens	count on	count back
subtract	difference	minus

Derive and recall sums of multiples of 10

Building on previous learning

Before starting this unit check that the children can already:

☐ derive and recall all addition and subtraction facts for each number to at least 20

☐ calculate the value of an unknown in a number sentence

Learning objectives

■ Derive all addition facts up to 200 for multiples of 10

Learning outcomes

The children will be able to:

■ derive all addition facts for multiples of 10 from 10 to 100

■ recall all addition facts for multiples of 10 from 10 to 100

Success criteria

Can the children...

☐ create appropriate addition sentences for each randomly produced number?

☐ derive the addition facts for multiples of 10 from 10 to 100?

☐ remember the addition facts multiples of 10 from 10 to 100?

☐ listen and talk confidently using some of the vocabulary listed?

How to use the material for discussion

A three-digit target number of a multiple of 10 will be displayed. The children's task is to create addition sentences with a total of the number shown. As with all of the activities the teacher can start the discussion using appropriate vocabulary and questions but should then encourage the pupils to take turns in leading the discussion. Encourage the children to produce several addition sentences for each number. This activity can be repeated regularly and would be very useful as a lesson starter.

The activity consists of the teacher, or a pupil playing the role of leader, asking pupils to create addition sentences to match a target number. The leader asks one of the other pupils for a number to start an addition number sentence – they will soon realise that this first number must be less than or equal to the focus number. They can collect this number from the number bank then insert the addition sign and ask another pupil for the number that will make the total of the target number, using questions such as 'What should I add to 120 to make 160?'.

They should complete the addition sentence with the equals sign and a copy of the target number, then read the whole sentence eg '120 add 40 equals 160' or '120 plus 40 equals 160' or 'the total of 120 and 40 is 160'.

Now another child could take the role of leader. Once several number sentences have been created for the target number, a new target number can be displayed by clicking the top right hand arrow.

Appropriate vocabulary

sign	symbol	addition
one-digit number	two-digit number	equals
addition sentence	number sentence	ones
tens	count on	add
sum	total	plus

Derive and recall all subtraction facts for multiples of 10

Building on previous learning

Before starting this unit check that the children can already:

☐ derive and recall all addition and subtraction facts for each number to at least 20

☐ calculate the value of an unknown in a number sentence

☐ derive all addition facts up to 200 for multiples of 10

Learning objectives

■ Derive all subtraction facts for multiples of 10 up to 200

Learning outcomes

The children will be able to:

■ derive all subtraction facts for multiples of 10 up to 200

■ recall all subtraction facts for multiples of 10 up to 200

Success criteria

Can the children…

☐ create appropriate subtraction sentences for each randomly produced number?

☐ derive the subtraction facts for multiples of 10 to 200?

☐ remember the subtraction facts for multiples of 10 to 200?

☐ listen and talk confidently using some of the vocabulary listed?

How to use the material for discussion

A three-digit target number of a multiple of 10 will be displayed. The children's task is to create subtraction sentences. As with all of the activities the teacher can start the discussion using appropriate vocabulary and questions but should then encourage the pupils to take turns in leading the discussion. Encourage the children to produce several subtraction sentences for each number. This activity can be repeated regularly and would be very useful as a lesson starter.

The activity consists of the teacher, or a pupil playing the role of leader, asking pupils to create subtraction sentences to match a target number. The leader asks one of the other pupils for a number to start a subtraction number sentence – they will soon realise that this first number must be the same as the target number. They can collect this number from the number bank then insert the subtraction sign and ask another pupil for a number to subtract from the target number.

They should read the subtraction using vocabulary such as '180 subtract 150' or '180 minus 150' or 'What is the difference between 180 and 150?'. They should then ask another child to complete the subtraction sentence with the equals sign and the answer.

Now another child could take the role of leader. Once several number sentences have been created for the target number, a new target number can be displayed by clicking the top right hand arrow.

Appropriate vocabulary

sign	symbol	subtraction
one-digit number	two-digit number	three-digit number
equals	subtraction sentence	number sentence
ones	tens	hundreds
count on	count back	subtract
difference	minus	

Derive and recall all number pairs that total 100

Building on previous learning

Before starting this unit check that the children can already:

☐ derive and recall all addition and subtraction facts for each number to at least 20

☐ derive and recall sums and differences of multiples of 10

☐ calculate the value of an unknown in a number sentence

Learning objectives

- Derive and recall all number pairs that total 100

- Use knowledge of number operations and corresponding inverses, including doubling and halving, to estimate and check calculations

Learning outcomes

The children will be able to:

- derive all number pairs that total 100
- recall all number pairs that total 100
- relate subtraction facts to addition facts

Success criteria

Can the children...

☐ devise appropriate addition sentences to create a total of 100?

☐ derive the corresponding subtraction facts?

☐ listen and talk confidently using some of the vocabulary listed?

How to use the material for discussion

The children's task is to create addition and subtraction sentences combining pairs of numbers with a total of 100. As with all of the activities the teacher can start the discussion using appropriate vocabulary and questions but should then encourage the pupils to take turns in leading the discussion. This activity can be repeated regularly and would be very useful as a lesson starter, consolidating pupils' awareness of inverse operations.

Let's Talk Maths
Year 3: Activity 10

Objective   Vocabulary   Instructions

100

100	–	80	=	
100	–		=	10
100	–		=	9
	–	70	=	30

0 10 18 20 29 30 36 40 42 50   =
58 60 64 70 71 80 82 90 91 100   + –

The activity consists of the teacher, or a pupil playing the role of leader, asking pupils to create addition and subtraction sentences related to 100. The leader should ask another pupil for the numbers that will make the total of 100. They should then ask other pupils to help them to complete the subtraction sentences by inserting the appropriate numbers.

Appropriate vocabulary

sign	symbol	addition
one-digit number	two-digit number	equals
addition sentence	number sentence	ones
tens	count on	add
sum	total	plus
subtraction	minus	subtract
difference		

Solve one-step and two-step problems involving money, choosing and carrying out appropriate calculations

Building on previous learning

Before starting this unit check that the children can already:

☐ derive and recall all addition and subtraction facts for each number to at least 20

☐ derive and recall sums and differences of multiples of 10

☐ derive and recall all number pairs that total 100

☐ use knowledge of number operations and corresponding inverses, including doubling and halving, to estimate and check calculations

Learning objectives

■ Solve problems involving adding in the context of money

■ Solve problems involving subtracting in the context of money

■ Solve one-step problems such as finding the total of or the difference between two amounts of money

■ Solve two-step problems such as finding the total of two amounts of money then the change from £1 when this total is spent

Learning outcomes

The children will be able to:

■ find total amounts to pay for two items

■ find change from £1 when buying an item

■ find differences in price between pairs of items

■ find the total price of two items, then the change from £1

Success criteria

Can the children…

☐ add together two sums of money in pence to find the total cost of two priced items?

☐ find the change from £1 when buying some priced items?

☐ use appropriate vocabulary in relation to spending money and finding change?

How to use the material for discussion

Pairs of priced items will be displayed for pupils to find total costs of, to make comparisons of and to find change from £1. With confident pupils you may wish to devise problems in relation to the priced items using all four number operations.

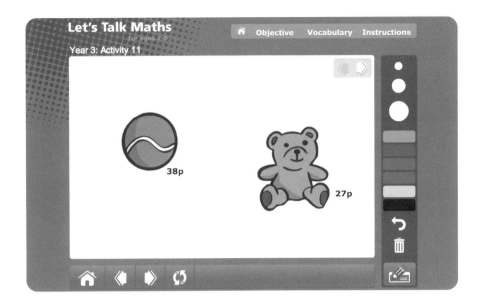

The items appear on the screen two at a time giving opportunities to discuss each one in relation to £1 and to each other. Discuss the items asking questions such as:

- How much change would I have from one pound if I bought the toy car?
- Which costs more, the bear or the ball? How much more?
- How much would both items cost altogether? Is that more than or less than £1? How much more/less?
- How much would three toy cars cost altogether?
- How much would four balls cost altogether?

Now ask one of the pupils to think of some questions to ask the other pupils.

Appropriate vocabulary

more	less	total
cost	altogether	difference
price	change	double
answer	explain	operation
pound	penny	pence
coin	add	subtract
multiply	double	calculate

Solve problems involving numbers and measures, including time, choosing and carrying out appropriate calculations

Building on previous learning

Before starting this unit check that the children can already:

- [ ] derive and recall all addition and subtraction facts for each number to at least 20
- [ ] derive and recall sums and differences of multiples of 10
- [ ] derive and recall all number pairs that total 100
- [ ] use knowledge of number operations and corresponding inverses, including doubling and halving, to estimate and check calculations
- [ ] count on or back in ones, twos, fives and tens
- [ ] recognise multiples of five

Learning objectives

- Solve problems involving numbers and measures, including time, choosing and carrying out appropriate calculations
- Read the time to the nearest 5 minutes on an analogue clock
- Calculate time intervals and find start or end times for a given time interval

Learning outcomes

The children will be able to:

- read the time to the nearest 5 minutes on an analogue clock
- solve problems involving calculation of time intervals

Success criteria

Can the children…

- [ ] read the time to the nearest 5 minutes on an analogue clock?
- [ ] find the number of minutes after the hour and the corresponding number of minutes to the next hour?
- [ ] state the end time for a given time interval when a start time is provided?
- [ ] state the start time for a given time interval when an end time is provided?

How to use the material for discussion

It is suggested that this activity is repeated over several short sessions, each session showing progression from the previous one. Showing the clock face at different times can be used for discussions using appropriate vocabulary.

Confident pupils will be able to find start or end times for a given time interval that crosses an o'clock time.

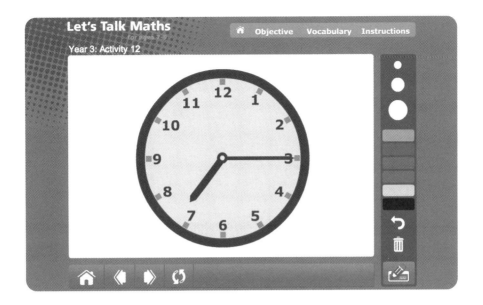

Many Year 3 pupils are not able to recognise times to the nearest five minutes. This should be the focus of the task the first time this activity is used. Ensure that the children can see that the time is being counted in multiples of 5 minutes when considering the numerals around the face.

The next time you use this activity encourage them to notice the position of the hour hand - ie that it has moved part way between one hour and the next. As an example, the clock shown above could be discussed with questions such as:

- How many minutes past five o'clock does the clock show?
- How many minutes will it be until six o'clock?

Once you feel that the pupils are confident, ask questions such as:

- What time does the clock show?
- What will the time be twenty minutes after that?
- What would the time have been twenty minutes before that time?

Appropriate vocabulary

count on	count back	multiple
clock	o'clock	quarter
half	hour	minutes
time	before	after
interval	start time	end time
hands	morning	afternoon
evening	midnight	midday
noon	night	day
whole turn	quarter turn	quarter to
half turn	quarter past	half-past

Derive and recall multiplication facts for the 3 times table and related division facts

Building on previous learning

Before starting this unit check that the children can already:

☐ derive and recall multiplication facts for the 2, 5 and 10 times tables and related division facts

☐ use the symbols x and = to record and interpret number sentences involving multiplication

☐ use the symbols ÷ and = to record and interpret number sentences involving division

Learning objectives

- derive multiplication facts for the 3 times table
- recall multiplication facts for the 3 times table
- derive division facts related to the 3 times table
- recall division facts related to the 3 times table
- understand that division is the inverse of multiplication and vice versa; use this to derive and record related multiplication and division number sentences

Learning outcomes

The children will be able to:

- derive and recall all multiplication and division facts for the 3 times table

Success criteria

Can the children...

☐ create number sentences on screen using the numerals and symbols to show the 3 times table?

☐ find related division facts?

How to use the material for discussion

This activity concerns raising pupils' confidence in mental arithmetic skills by constructing the 3 times table and finding the corresponding division facts. Practising number facts, understanding the vocabulary and methods of recording, can give pupils the tools with which to deal with more complex mathematical problems. Note that Year 3 pupils will need further practice in the 2, 5 and 10 times tables – these are featured in Let's Talk Maths for ages 5–7.

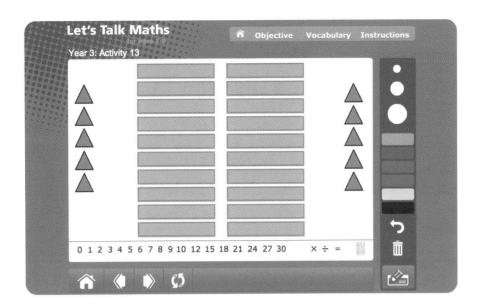

Discuss the triangles. Ask the children why we might look at triangles when we are discussing the 3 times table – hopefully they will say that each triangle has 3 sides and 3 vertices. Discuss the fact that 2 triangles will have 6 vertices altogether. Ask the children to take turns to record a part of the 3 times table. As with all of these activities, encourage each child to ask the questions clearly using the appropriate vocabulary. Once the 3 times table is complete ask the children to find the corresponding division facts and to record these alongside the table.

Appropriate vocabulary

pair	multiply	divide
equals	times	share
sign	explain	number sentence
write	record	the same number as
calculate	calculation	operation
answer	inverse	pattern
triangle	corner	explain

Derive and recall multiplication facts for the 4 times table and related division facts

Building on previous learning

Before starting this unit check that the children can already:

☐ derive and recall multiplication facts for the 2, 3, 5 and 10 times tables and related division facts

☐ use the symbols x and = to record and interpret number sentences involving multiplication

☐ use the symbols ÷ and = to record and interpret number sentences involving division

Learning objectives

■ derive multiplication facts for the 4 times table

■ recall multiplication facts for the 4 times table

■ derive division facts related to the 4 times table

■ recall division facts related to the 4 times table

■ understand that division is the inverse of multiplication and vice versa; use this to derive and record related multiplication and division number sentences

Learning outcomes

The children will be able to:

■ derive and recall all multiplication and division facts for the 4 times table

Success criteria

Can the children…

☐ create number sentences on screen using the numerals and symbols to show the 4 times table?

☐ find related division facts?

How to use the material for discussion

This activity concerns raising pupils' confidence in mental arithmetic skills by constructing the 4 times table and finding the corresponding division facts. Practising number facts, understanding the vocabulary and methods of recording, can give pupils the tools with which to deal with more complex mathematical problems. Note that Year 3 pupils will need further practice in the 2, 5 and 10 times tables – these are featured in Let's Talk Maths for ages 5–7.

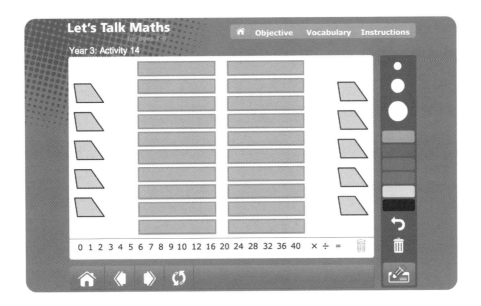

Discuss the quadrilaterals. Ask the children why we might look at quadrilaterals when we are discussing the 4 times table – hopefully they will say that each quadrilateral has 4 sides and 4 vertices. Discuss the fact that 2 quadrilaterals will have 8 vertices altogether. Ask the children to take turns to record a part of the 4 times table. As with all of these activities, encourage each child to ask the questions clearly using the appropriate vocabulary. Once the 4 times table is complete ask the children to find the corresponding division facts and to record these alongside the table.

Appropriate vocabulary

pair	multiply	divide
equals	times	share
sign	explain	number sentence
write	record	the same number as
calculate	calculation	operation
answer	inverse	pattern
quadrilateral	corner	explain

Derive and recall multiplication facts for the 6 times table and related division facts

Building on previous learning

Before starting this unit check that the children can already:

☐ derive and recall multiplication facts for the 2, 3, 4, 5 and 10 times-tables and related division facts

☐ use the symbols x and = to record and interpret number sentences involving multiplication

☐ use the symbols ÷ and = to record and interpret number sentences involving division

Learning objectives

- derive multiplication facts for the 6 times table

- recall multiplication facts for the 6 times table

- derive division facts related to the 6 times table

- recall division facts related to the 6 times table

- understand that division is the inverse of multiplication and vice versa; use this to derive and record related multiplication and division number sentences

Learning outcomes

The children will be able to:

- derive and recall all multiplication and division facts for the 6 times table

Success criteria

Can the children...

☐ create number sentences on screen using the numerals and symbols to show the 6 times table?

☐ find related division facts?

How to use the material for discussion

This activity concerns raising pupils' confidence in mental arithmetic skills by constructing the 6 times table and finding the corresponding division facts. Practising number facts, understanding the vocabulary and methods of recording, can give pupils the tools with which to deal with more complex mathematical problems. Note that Year 3 pupils will need further practice in the 2, 5 and 10 times tables – these are featured in Let's Talk Maths for ages 5–7.

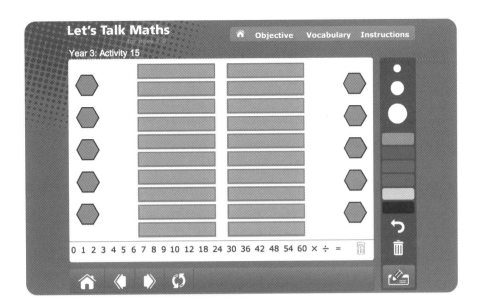

Discuss the hexagons. Ask the children why we might look at hexagons when we are discussing the 6 times table – hopefully they will say that each hexagon has 6 sides and 6 vertices. Discuss the fact that 2 hexagons will have 12 vertices altogether. Ask the children to take turns to record a part of the 6 times table. As with all of these activities, encourage each child to ask the questions clearly using the appropriate vocabulary. Once the 6 times table is complete ask the children to find the corresponding division facts and to record these alongside the table.

Appropriate vocabulary

pair	multiply	divide
equals	times	share
sign	explain	number sentence
write	record	the same number as
calculate	calculation	operation
answer	inverse	pattern
hexagon	corner	explain
vertex	vertices	

Relate 2-D shapes to drawings of them; describe, visualise, classify, draw and make the shapes

Building on previous learning

Before starting this unit check that the children can already:

- [ ] visualise and name common 2-D shapes and describe their features
- [ ] sort, make and describe shapes referring to their properties
- [ ] identify reflective symmetry in patterns and 2-D shapes

Learning objectives

- Identify shapes from pictures of them in different positions and orientations
- Visualise, draw, make and describe shapes referring to their properties

Learning outcomes

The children will be able to:

- identify 2-D shapes on screen
- use appropriate vocabulary to refer to the properties of the shapes
- visualise, draw, make and describe the following shapes: square, triangle, rectangle, quadrilateral, pentagon, hexagon, octagon, circle, semicircle

Success criteria

Can the children...

- [ ] identify 2-D shapes, using appropriate vocabulary to refer to their properties?
- [ ] visualise, draw, make and describe a square, triangle, rectangle, quadrilateral, pentagon, hexagon, octagon, circle, semicircle?

How to use the material for discussion

The following shapes are displayed: square, triangle, rectangle, quadrilateral, pentagon, hexagon, octagon, circle, semicircle. The task is for the pupils to identify the shape and describe its properties. Note that there is more than one version of each of the shapes to encourage discussion.

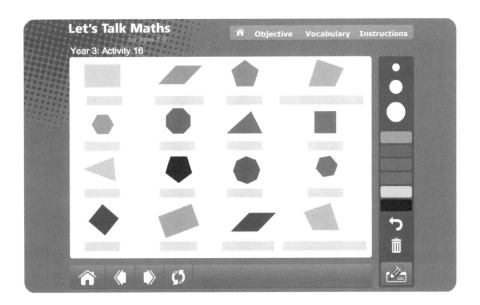

Ask one of the children to point to a shape and, without naming it, describe one property that the shape possesses, eg the number of sides or the number of vertices. Ask another pupil to describe a different property of the shape. Encourage the children to state whether the sides are equal in length and whether the shape has reflective symmetry. Once all the properties of the shape have been discussed ask the pupils to give the name of the shape. Note that there are several quadrilaterals, including squares and rectangles in different orientations. Click on the grey box under the shape to reveal the name.

Appropriate vocabulary

triangle	quadrilateral	rectangle
hexagon	corner	side
straight	curved	shape
line of symmetry	mirror line	reflection
square	rectangular	triangular
pentagon	octagon	edge
property	explain	describe
circle	semicircle	symmetrical
reflective symmetry	right-angled	vertex
vertices		

Draw and complete shapes with reflective symmetry; draw the reflection of a shape in a mirror line along one side

Building on previous learning

Before starting this unit check that the children can already:

- [ ] visualise and name common 2-D shapes and describe their features
- [ ] identify shapes from pictures of them in different positions and orientations
- [ ] sort, make and describe shapes referring to their properties
- [ ] identify reflective symmetry in patterns and 2-D shapes

Learning objectives

- Draw and complete shapes with reflective symmetry
- Draw the reflection of a shape in a mirror line along one side

Learning outcomes

The children will be able to:

- create symmetrical shapes and patterns on a grid
- use appropriate vocabulary in relation to symmetry

Success criteria

Can the children…

- [ ] create symmetrical shapes and patterns on a grid?
- [ ] use appropriate vocabulary in relation to symmetry?

How to use the material for discussion

When a square on the grid is touched it will change colour enabling pupils to create symmetrical patterns. Encourage them to use the appropriate vocabulary in relation to their pictures.

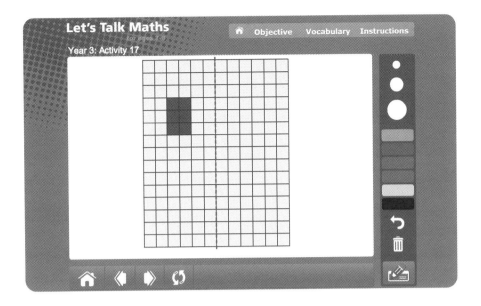

Invite the children to come to the screen to create symmetrical patterns by touching the squares on the grid. You may wish to suggest that one child should touch a set of squares randomly then another child should try to make a symmetrical pattern by touching the corresponding squares. Some children will need help in finding the corresponding squares and will need guidance in counting squares and the distances from the mirror line. Encourage the children to use the appropriate vocabulary.

Appropriate vocabulary

shape	line of symmetry	mirror line
reflection	square	rectangular
right-angled	property	explain describe
symmetrical	reflective symmetry	vertex
vertices		

Read and write proper fractions, interpreting the denominator as the parts of a whole and the numerator as the number of parts

Building on previous learning

Before starting this unit check that the children can already:

☐ use the vocabulary of halves and quarters in context, eg when discussing food items such as cakes, pizzas, apples, bars of chocolate, etc

☐ find one half, one quarter and three quarters of shapes and sets of objects

Learning objectives

- Read proper fractions
- Create proper fractions on screen
- Interpret the denominator as parts of a whole
- Interpret the numerator as the number of parts

Learning outcomes

The children will be able to:

- count the number of parts of a whole circle, cut in sectors, to determine the denominator of a fraction
- count the number of shaded sectors of the circle to determine the numerator of a fraction

Success criteria

Can the children...

☐ create fractions on screen by counting the number of parts of a whole to determine the denominator and the number of shaded parts to determine the numerator?

☐ use appropriate vocabulary to discuss the fractions?

How to use the material for discussion

Before doing the activity, take the opportunity to discuss real items that can be cut into parts, eg pizzas, cakes, etc. Circles that have been cut into equal sectors and that have some of the sectors shaded will be displayed. The pupils' task is to determine the fraction of each circle that is shaded – you may also wish to ask them what fraction is not shaded.

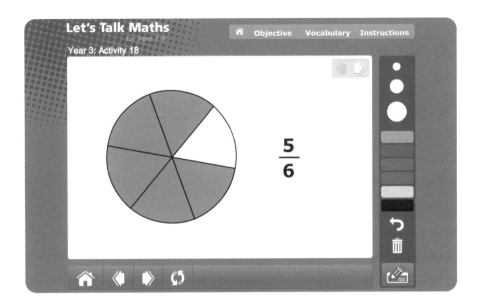

An example is displayed on the first screen of this activity. When a pupil touches the top right hand arrow two circles cut into equal parts will appear on the screen; some of the parts are shaded. It is important to discuss the 'whole' circle, then to ask how many equal parts it has – encourage the children to refer to 'parts of the whole' circle. Now ask a child to write a number in the lower part of the fraction to show the number of parts of the whole. Ask another child to write a number in the upper part of the fraction to show the 'number of parts' that are shaded. Now discuss the fraction that has been created. Note that the vocabulary list for Year 3 does not use the words 'numerator' or 'denominator' but instead refers to 'number of parts' and 'parts of a whole' respectively.

One of the children can now take over as 'leader': asking others to create the fractions and all the time using the appropriate vocabulary.

Appropriate vocabulary

fraction	part	equal parts
one whole	parts of a whole	number of parts
one half	one quarter	three quarters
one sixth	five sixths	one fifth
two fifths	three fifths	four fifths
one tenth	two tenths	three tenths
four tenths	six tenths	seven tenths
eight tenths	nine tenths	

Order four-digit whole numbers

Building on previous learning

Before starting this unit check that the children can already:

☐ read and write two-digit and three-digit numbers in figures and words

☐ relate all these to the number line

Learning objectives

■ Order four-digit whole numbers

Learning outcomes

The children will be able to:

■ interpret the value of each digit in a four-digit number

■ place five four-digit numbers in order

■ use appropriate vocabulary

■ talk confidently about the numbers

Success criteria

Can the children…

☐ read confidently the numbers pointed out to them?

☐ arrange the numbers in order from smallest to biggest or from biggest to smallest?

☐ listen and talk confidently using some of the vocabulary listed and some of the question types shown?

How to use the material for discussion

The adult should start with asking questions to provide a structure but should try to withdraw from the discussion and allow the children to take over so that they are asking questions of each other. They will, at times, need to be reminded of the appropriate vocabulary and you may wish to encourage them to use the vocabulary listed.

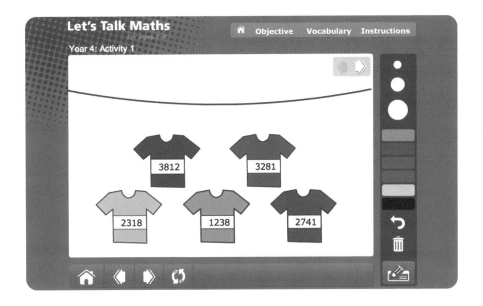

The activity could open with questions of the following type:

- What is this number? Can you read this number?
- How many digits does this number have?

If you feel that the children are confident, different questions can be used:

- What number is one more than this number?
- What number is one less than this number?
- What number is ten more than this number?
- What number is ten less than this number?
- What number is one hundred more than this number?
- What number is one hundred less than this number?
- What number is one thousand more than this number?
- What number is one thousand less than this number?
- Can you count up from this number in tens?

Now ask which number should be first if we wish to 'hang' the t-shirts on the washing line in order starting with the smallest. Ask another child which number should come next. Ensure that the children discuss the place value of the digits and that they realise that the thousands digit will be the most important one to consider first. When all the numbers have been put in order on the washing line from smallest to biggest, ask a child to be the leader with a new set of numbers.

Appropriate vocabulary

explain	digit	pattern
place value	ones	tens
hundreds	thousand	one-digit number
two-digit number	three-digit number	four-digit number
predict	reason	partition
compare	order	greater than
less than		

Partition four-digit numbers into multiples of 1000, 100, 10 and 1

Building on previous learning

Before starting this unit check that the children can already:

☐ read and write two-digit and three-digit numbers

☐ relate two-digit and three-digit numbers to a number line

Learning objectives

■ Partition four-digit numbers into multiples of 1000, 100, 10 and 1. (Note that Year 4 Activity 2 encourages children to observe how four-digit numbers can be seen to constitute thousands, hundreds, tens and ones – this understanding leads to the ability to partition.)

Learning outcomes

The children will be able to:

■ read four-digit numbers in figures

■ use appropriate vocabulary

■ talk confidently about the numbers

■ 'build' four-digit numbers by combining thousands, hundreds, tens and ones

Success criteria

Can the children…

☐ build specified four-digit numbers?

☐ listen and talk confidently using some of the vocabulary listed and some of the question types shown?

How to use the material for discussion

The adult should start with asking questions to provide a structure but should try to withdraw from the discussion and allow the children to take over so that they are asking questions of each other. They will, at times, need to be reminded of the appropriate vocabulary and you may wish to encourage them to use the vocabulary listed.

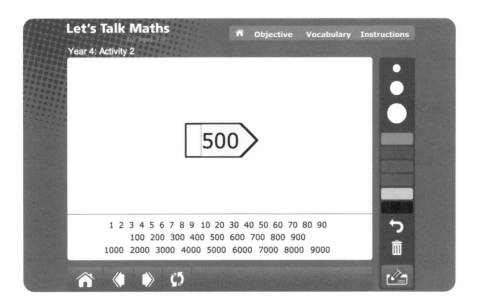

The activity consists of the teacher, or a pupil playing the role of leader, asking pupils to build a specified four-digit number, eg:

- Can you make the number 3842?

A pupil then comes to the screen and drags the appropriate numbers to the place value box where the numbers merge to make the number specified.

A further feature of the activity is that the constituent parts of the number can be taken away. For example, ask the child to take away 40 from 3842 – if s/he drags the 40 away the 3802 will remain in the centre box.

Appropriate vocabulary

explain	reasoning	pattern
predict	reason	place value
partition	thousands	digit
four-digit number	compare	order
greater than	less than	

Round four-digit numbers to the nearest 10, 100 or 1000

Building on previous learning

Before starting this unit check that the children can already:

- [ ] read and write two-digit, three-digit and four-digit numbers
- [ ] read numbers from 0 to 10000
- [ ] recognise multiples of 5 and 10
- [ ] round two-digit numbers to the nearest 10
- [ ] round three-digit numbers to the nearest 100
- [ ] round three-digit numbers to the nearest 100 or 10

Learning objectives

- Round four-digit numbers to the nearest 1000, 100 or 10

Learning outcomes

The children will be able to:

- round four-digit numbers up or down to the nearest multiple of 1000
- round up to the nearest 1000 from a multiple of 500
- round four-digit numbers up or down to the nearest multiple of 100
- round up to the nearest 100 from a multiple of 50
- round four-digit numbers up or down to the nearest multiple of 10
- round up to the nearest 10 from a multiple of 5

Success criteria

Can the children…

- [ ] round four-digit numbers up or down to the nearest multiple of 1000?
- [ ] round up to the nearest 1000 from a multiple of 500?
- [ ] round four-digit numbers up or down to the nearest multiple of 100?
- [ ] round up to the nearest 100 from a multiple of 50?
- [ ] round four-digit numbers up or down to the nearest multiple of 10?
- [ ] listen and talk confidently using some of the vocabulary listed?

How to use the material for discussion

This activity should be used with the pupils once they are confident with the activities in Year 3 Activity 5, Year 4 Activity 1 and Year 4 Activity 2. The task is for the children to round four-digit numbers to the nearest multiple of 1000. Many children will find the next steps more difficult – matching the four-digit numbers to the nearest multiple of 100 or to the nearest multiple of 10. As with all of the activities the teacher can start the discussion using appropriate vocabulary and questions but should then encourage the pupils to take turns in leading the discussion.

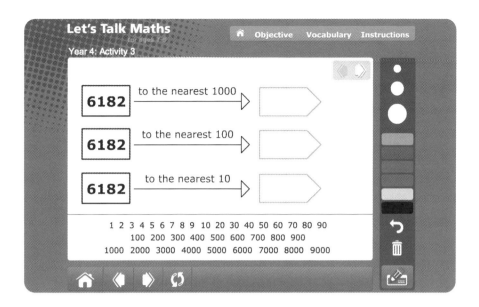

This activity consists of the teacher, or a pupil playing the role of leader, asking pupils to round a four-digit number to the nearest 1000, to the nearest 100 and to the nearest 10. Children should first discuss to which multiple of 1000, 100 or 10 the number displayed in the left hand box is closest to. A child should then drag the appropriate multiple of 1000, 100 and 10 from the bank at the bottom of the screen into the appropriate place value box. By clicking on the top right hand arrow a new four-digit number will be displayed.

Appropriate vocabulary

pattern	place value	digit
ones	tens	hundreds
thousands	four-digit number	
one-digit number	two-digit number	three-digit number
compare	order	round
nearest	approximate	estimate

Recognise and continue number sequences formed by counting on or back in steps of constant size

Building on previous learning

Before starting this unit check that the children can already:

☐ count on from or back to zero in single-digit steps or multiples of 10

☐ recognise multiples of 5 and 10

Learning objectives

■ Recognise and continue number sequences formed by counting on or back in steps of constant size

Learning outcomes

The children will be able to:

■ recognise and continue number sequences formed by counting on from any number in steps of constant size

■ recognise and continue number sequences formed by counting back from any number in steps of constant size

Success criteria

Can the children…

☐ identify properties of the numbers shown in the sequences?

☐ recognise that the sequences are formed by making steps of constant size?

☐ continue the sequences by suggesting two or more numbers to follow those shown?

☐ listen and talk confidently using some of the vocabulary listed?

How to use the material for discussion

In this activity children discuss number sequences. As with all of the activities the teacher can start the discussion using appropriate vocabulary and questions but should then encourage the pupils to take turns in leading the discussion.

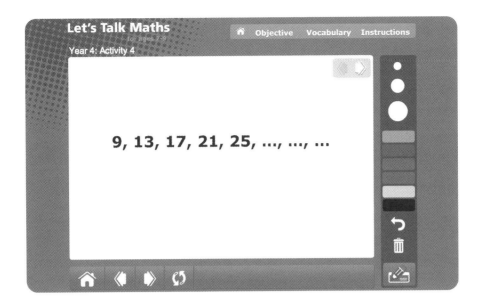

The activity consists of the teacher, or a pupil playing the role of leader, asking pupils to continue a sequence of numbers. Each sequence of numbers gives opportunities to discuss properties of numbers apart from just the sequence itself. For example, you could ask pupils what they can tell you about the sequence shown above. They may suggest that the numbers are all odd; they may point out that most of the numbers are two-digit numbers but that the first one is a one-digit number.

Ask them whether the numbers in the sequence are getting bigger or smaller. Ask what number step is needed to get from one number to the next – is it always this step in this sequence? Now can they identify the next two numbers that could appear in the sequence? Clicking on the top right hand arrow will display a new sequence.

Appropriate vocabulary

calculation	answer	method
explain	reasoning	pattern
predict	reason	rule
sequence	place value	digit
order	compare	add
subtract	constant	count on
count back		

Derive sums of multiples of 10

Building on previous learning

Before starting this unit check that the children can already:

☐ derive and recall all addition and subtraction facts for each number to at least 20

☐ derive all addition facts up to 200 for multiples of 10

Learning objectives

■ Use knowledge of addition facts and place value to derive sums up to 1000 for multiples of 10

Learning outcomes

The children will be able to:

■ derive sums of multiples of 10 from 10 to 1000

Success criteria

Can the children...

☐ derive sums of multiples of 10 to 1000?

☐ listen and talk confidently using some of the vocabulary listed?

How to use the material for discussion

The children will add multiples of 10 from 10 up to 500 to reach totals up to 1000. As with all of the activities the teacher can start the discussion using appropriate vocabulary and questions but should then encourage the pupils to take turns in leading the discussion. This activity can be repeated regularly and would be very useful as a lesson starter.

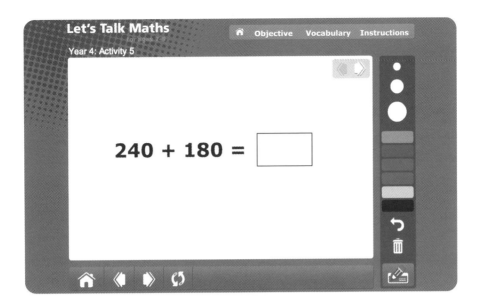

The activity consists of the teacher, or a pupil playing the role of leader, asking pupils to answer number sentence questions. Pupils give the answer orally and need to check each other's answers – this is a valuable part of the discussion.

Before asking the pupils to find the answers to the additions, encourage them to look closely at each of the numbers. How many digits does the number have? What is the value of the tens digit? What is the value of the hundreds digit?

Now encourage the children to explain how they could add the numbers together. Are they going to add the hundreds first? Are they going to add the tens first? Are they going to add the hundreds from the second number to the first number, then add the tens? Are they going to add the tens from the second number to the first number, then add the hundreds? Which way do they find quickest?

Appropriate vocabulary

calculate	calculation	equation
operation	answer	method
explain	reasoning	pattern
predict	reason	rule
place value	partition	digit
two-digit number	three-digit number	add
sum	total	plus

Derive differences between multiples of 10

Building on previous learning

Before starting this unit check that the children can already:

☐ derive and recall all addition and subtraction facts for each number to at least 20

☐ derive all addition and subtraction facts up to 200 for multiples of 10

Learning objectives

■ Use knowledge of addition and subtraction facts and place value to derive differences up to 1000 for multiples of 10

Learning outcomes

The children will be able to:

■ derive differences between multiples of 10 from 10 to 1000

Success criteria

Can the children...

☐ derive differences between multiples of 10 to 1000?

☐ listen and talk confidently using some of the vocabulary listed?

How to use the material for discussion

The children will find the difference between multiples of 10 from 10 up to 1000. As with all of the activities the teacher can start the discussion using appropriate vocabulary and questions but should then encourage the pupils to take turns in leading the discussion. This activity can be repeated regularly and would be very useful as a lesson starter.

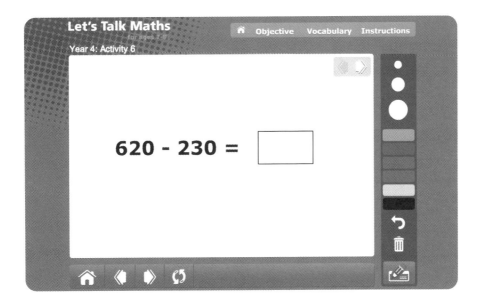

The activity consists of the teacher, or a pupil playing the role of leader, asking pupils to answer number sentence questions. Pupils give the answer orally and need to check each other's answers – this is a valuable part of the discussion.

Before asking the pupils to find the answers to the subtractions, encourage them to look closely at each of the numbers. How many digits does the number have? What is the value of the tens digit? What is the value of the hundreds digit?

Now encourage the children to explain how they could find the differences between them. Are they going to count on in tens from the smaller to the greater number? Are they going to count back? Are they going to use an empty number line? Which way do they find quickest?

Appropriate vocabulary

calculate	calculation	equation
operation	answer	method
explain	reasoning	pattern
predict	reason	rule
place value	partition	digit
two-digit number	three-digit number	subtract
difference	minus	

Derive sums of multiples of 100 or 1000

Building on previous learning

Before starting this unit check that the children can already:

- ☐ derive and recall all addition and subtraction facts for each number to at least 20
- ☐ derive all addition facts up to 200 for multiples of 10
- ☐ use knowledge of addition facts and place value to derive sums up to 1000 for multiples of 10

Learning objectives

- ■ Use knowledge of addition facts and place value to derive sums of pairs of multiples of 100 or 1000

Learning outcomes

The children will be able to:

- ■ derive sums of pairs of multiples of 100 or 1000

Success criteria

Can the children…

- ☐ derive sums of multiples of 100 or 1000?
- ☐ listen and talk confidently using some of the vocabulary listed?

How to use the material for discussion

The children will add multiples of 100 or 1000 from 500 up to 5000 to reach totals up to 10000. As with all of the activities the teacher can start the discussion using appropriate vocabulary and questions but should then encourage the pupils to take turns in leading the discussion. This activity can be repeated regularly and would be very useful as a lesson starter.

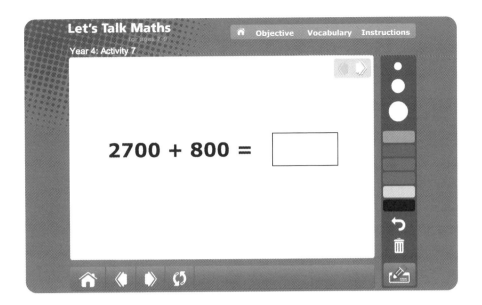

The activity consists of the teacher, or a pupil playing the role of leader, asking pupils to answer number sentence questions. Pupils give the answer orally and need to check each other's answers – this is a valuable part of the discussion.

Before asking the pupils to find the answers to the additions, encourage them to look closely at each of the numbers. How many digits does the number have? What is the value of the thousands digit? What is the value of the hundreds digit?

Now encourage the children to explain how they could add the numbers together. Are they going to add the hundreds first? Are they going to add the thousands first? Are they going to add the hundreds from the second number to the first number, then add the thousands? Are they going to add the thousands from the second number to the first number, then add the hundreds? Which way do they find quickest?

Appropriate vocabulary

calculate	calculation	equation
operation	answer	method
explain	reasoning	pattern
predict	reason	rule
place value	partition	digit
two-digit number	three-digit number	add
sum	total	plus
four-digit number	thousands	

Blocks   A, B and revision

Derive differences between multiples of 100 or 1000

Building on previous learning

Before starting this unit check that the children can already:

☐ derive and recall all addition and subtraction facts for each number to at least 20

☐ derive all addition and subtraction facts up to 200 for multiples of 10

☐ use knowledge of addition and subtraction facts and place value to derive differences up to 1000 for multiples of 10

Learning objectives

■ Use knowledge of addition and subtraction facts and place value to derive differences between multiples of 100 or 1000 up to 10000

Learning outcomes

The children will be able to:

■ derive differences between multiples of 100 or 1000 up to 10000

Success criteria

Can the children...

☐ derive differences between multiples of 100 or 1000 up to 10000?

☐ listen and talk confidently using some of the vocabulary listed?

How to use the material for discussion

The children will find the difference between pairs of multiples of 100 or 1000 up to 10000. As with all of the activities the teacher can start the discussion using appropriate vocabulary and questions but should then encourage the pupils to take turns in leading the discussion. This activity can be repeated regularly and would be very useful as a lesson starter.

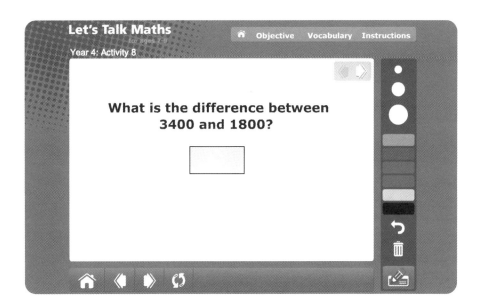

The activity consists of the teacher, or a pupil playing the role of leader, asking pupils to answer number sentence questions. Pupils give the answer orally and need to check each other's answers – this is a valuable part of the discussion.

Before asking the pupils to find the answers to the subtractions, encourage them to look closely at each of the numbers. How many digits does the number have? What is the value of the thousands digit? What is the value of the hundreds digit?

Now encourage the children to explain how they could find the differences between them. Are they going to count on in hundreds from the smaller to the greater number? Are they going to count back? Are they going to use an empty number line? Which way do they find quickest?

Appropriate vocabulary

calculate	calculation	equation
operation	answer	method
explain	reasoning	pattern
predict	reason	rule
place value	partition	digit
two-digit number	three-digit number	subtract
difference	minus	four-digit number

Add mentally pairs of two-digit whole numbers

Building on previous learning

Before starting this unit check that the children can already:

☐ derive and recall all addition and subtraction facts for each number to at least 20

☐ derive and recall all addition facts up to 200 for multiples of 10

☐ use knowledge of addition facts and place value to derive sums up to 1000 for multiples of 10

Learning objectives

■ Add mentally pairs of two-digit whole numbers

Learning outcomes

The children will be able to:

■ refine and use their own strategies to add mentally pairs of two-digit whole numbers

Success criteria

Can the children…

☐ add mentally pairs of two-digit whole numbers?

☐ listen and talk confidently using some of the vocabulary listed?

How to use the material for discussion

Children will add together mentally pairs of two-digit numbers. As with all of the activities the teacher can start the discussion using appropriate vocabulary and questions but should then encourage the pupils to take turns in leading the discussion. This activity can be repeated regularly and would be very useful as a lesson starter.

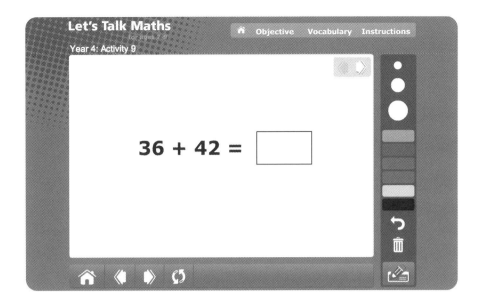

The activity consists of the teacher, or a pupil playing the role of leader, asking pupils to answer number sentence questions. Pupils give the answer orally and need to check each other's answers – this is a valuable part of the discussion.

Before asking the pupils to find the answers to the additions, encourage them to look closely at each of the numbers. How many digits does the number have? What is the value of the tens digit? What is the value of the ones (or units) digit?

Now encourage the children to explain how they could add the numbers together. Are they going to add the tens first? Are they going to add the ones first? Are they going to add the tens from the second number to the first number, then add the ones? Are they going to add the ones from the second number to the first number, then add the tens? Which way do they find quickest?

Appropriate vocabulary

calculate	calculation	equation
operation	answer	method
explain	reasoning	pattern
predict	reason	rule
place value	partition	digit
two-digit number	three-digit number	add
sum	total	plus

Subtract mentally pairs of two-digit whole numbers

Building on previous learning

Before starting this unit check that the children can already:

- [ ] derive and recall all addition and subtraction facts for each number to at least 20
- [ ] derive all addition and subtraction facts up to 200 for multiples of 10
- [ ] use knowledge of addition and subtraction facts and place value to derive differences up to 1000 for multiples of 10

Learning objectives

- Subtract mentally pairs of two-digit whole numbers

Learning outcomes

The children will be able to:

- subtract mentally pairs of two-digit whole numbers

Success criteria

Can the children...

- [ ] subtract mentally pairs of two-digit whole numbers?
- [ ] listen and talk confidently using some of the vocabulary listed?

How to use the material for discussion

The children will find the difference between pairs of two-digit numbers. As with all of the activities the teacher can start the discussion using appropriate vocabulary and questions but should then encourage the pupils to take turns in leading the discussion. This activity can be repeated regularly and would be very useful as a lesson starter.

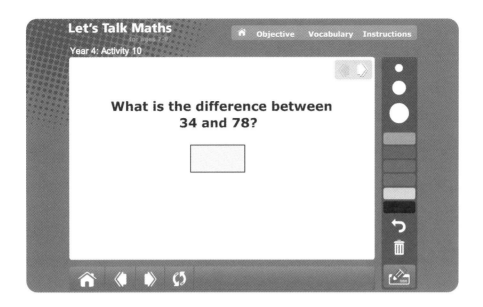

The activity consists of the teacher, or a pupil playing the role of leader, asking pupils to answer number sentence questions. Pupils give the answer orally and need to check each other's answers – this is a valuable part of the discussion.

Before asking the pupils to find the answers to the subtractions, encourage them to look closely at each of the numbers. Which is the bigger number? Are the two numbers close to each other on a number line?

Now encourage the children to explain how they could find the differences between them. Are they going to count on from the smaller to the greater number? Are they going to count back? Are they going to use a labelled number line or an empty number line? Which way do they find quickest?

Appropriate vocabulary

calculate	calculation	equation
operation	answer	method
explain	reasoning	pattern
predict	reason	rule
place value	partition	digit
two-digit number	subtract	
difference	minus	

Derive and recall multiplication facts for the 7 times table and related division facts

Building on previous learning

Before starting this unit check that the children can already:

☐ derive and recall multiplication facts for the 2, 3, 4, 5, 6 and 10 times tables and related division facts

☐ use the symbols x and = to record and interpret number sentences involving multiplication

☐ use the symbols ÷ and = to record and interpret number sentences involving division

Learning objectives

■ derive multiplication facts for the 7 times table

■ recall multiplication facts for the 7 times table

■ derive division facts related to the 7 times table

■ recall division facts related to the 7 times table

■ understand that division is the inverse of multiplication and vice versa; use this to derive and record related multiplication and division number sentences

Learning outcomes

The children will be able to:

■ derive and recall all multiplication and division facts for the 7 times table

■ recognise heptagons and describe their properties

Success criteria

Can the children…

☐ create number sentences on screen using the numerals and symbols to show the 7 times table?

☐ find related division facts?

How to use the material for discussion

This activity concerns raising pupils' confidence in mental arithmetic skills by constructing the 7 times table and finding the corresponding division facts. Practising number facts, understanding the vocabulary and methods of recording, can give pupils the tools with which to deal with more complex mathematical problems. Note that Year 4 pupils will need further practice in the 2, 5 and 10 times tables (featured in Let's Talk Maths for ages 5–7) and in the 3, 4 and 6 times tables (featured in the Year 3 section of this book).

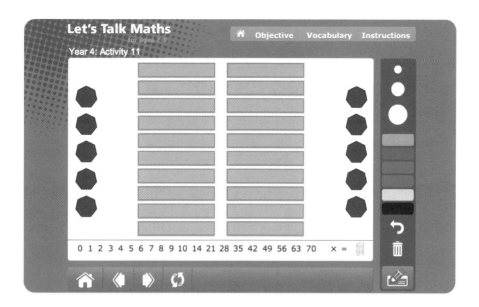

Discuss the heptagons. Ask the children why we might look at heptagons when we are discussing the 7 times table – hopefully they will say that each heptagon has 7 sides and 7 vertices. Discuss the fact that 2 heptagons will have 14 vertices altogether. Do the children know where we may find items in everyday use based on the shape of the heptagon? (The 20p and 50p coins are both based on heptagons but the sides are not straight.)

Ask the children to take turns to record a part of the 7 times table. As with all of these activities, encourage each child to ask the questions clearly using the appropriate vocabulary. Once the 7 times table is complete ask the children to find the corresponding division facts and to record these in the right hand column.

Appropriate vocabulary

pair	multiply	divide
equals	times	share
sign	explain	number sentence
write	record	the same number as
calculate	calculation	operation
answer	inverse	pattern
heptagon	corner	explain
vertex	vertices	

Derive and recall multiplication facts for the 8 times table and related division facts

Building on previous learning

Before starting this unit check that the children can already:

- [ ] derive and recall multiplication facts for the 2, 3, 4, 5, 6, 7 and 10 times tables and related division facts
- [ ] use the symbols x and = to record and interpret number sentences involving multiplication
- [ ] use the symbols ÷ and = to record and interpret number sentences involving division

Learning objectives

- derive multiplication facts for the 8 times table
- recall multiplication facts for the 8 times table
- derive division facts related to the 8 times table
- recall division facts related to the 8 times table
- understand that division is the inverse of multiplication and vice versa; use this to derive and record related multiplication and division number sentences

Learning outcomes

The children will be able to:

- derive and recall all multiplication and division facts for the 8 times table
- recognise octagons and describe their properties

Success criteria

Can the children...

- [ ] create number sentences on screen using the numerals and symbols to show the 8 times table?
- [ ] find related division facts?

How to use the material for discussion

This activity concerns raising pupils' confidence in mental arithmetic skills by constructing the 8 times table and finding the corresponding division facts. Practising number facts, understanding the vocabulary and methods of recording, can give pupils the tools with which to deal with more complex mathematical problems. Note that Year 4 pupils will need further practice in the 2, 5 and 10 times tables (featured in Let's Talk Maths for ages 5–7) and in the 3, 4 and 6 times tables (featured in the Year 3 section of this book).

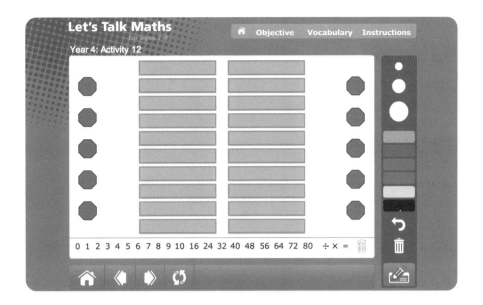

Discuss the octagons. Ask the children why we might look at octagons when we are discussing the 8 times table – hopefully they will say that each octagon has 8 sides and 8 vertices. Discuss the fact that 2 octagons will have 16 vertices altogether. Do the children know other words that start with the prefix 'oct'? Eg, octopus (8 legs), octuplets (8 babies born at one time), October (used to be the eighth month of the year in the Roman calendar), octave (8 musical notes).

Ask the children to take turns to record a part of the 8 times table. As with all of these activities, encourage each child to ask the questions clearly using the appropriate vocabulary. Once the 8 times table is complete ask the children to find the corresponding division facts and to record these alongside the table.

Appropriate vocabulary

pair	multiply	divide
equals	times	share
sign	explain	number sentence
write	record	the same number as
calculate	calculation	operation
answer	inverse	pattern
octagon	corner	explain
vertex	vertices	

Derive and recall multiplication facts for the 9 times table and related division facts

Building on previous learning

Before starting this unit check that the children can already:

☐ derive and recall multiplication facts for the 2, 3, 4, 5, 6, 7, 8 and 10 times-tables and related division facts

☐ use the symbols x and = to record and interpret number sentences involving multiplication

☐ use the symbols ÷ and = to record and interpret number sentences involving division

Learning objectives

■ derive multiplication facts for the 9 times table

■ recall multiplication facts for the 9 times table

■ derive division facts related to the 9 times table

■ recall division facts related to the 9 times table

■ understand that division is the inverse of multiplication and vice versa; use this to derive and record related multiplication and division number sentences

Learning outcomes

The children will be able to:

■ derive and recall all multiplication and division facts for the 9 times table

■ recognise nonagons and describe their properties

Success criteria

Can the children...

☐ create number sentences on screen using the numerals and symbols to show the 9 times table?

☐ find related division facts?

How to use the material for discussion

This activity concerns raising pupils' confidence in mental arithmetic skills by constructing the 9 times table and finding the corresponding division facts. Practising number facts, understanding the vocabulary and methods of recording, can give pupils the tools with which to deal with more complex mathematical problems. Note that Year 4 pupils will need further practice in the 2, 5 and 10 times tables (featured in Let's Talk Maths for ages 5–7) and in the 3, 4 and 6 times tables (featured in the Year 3 section of this book).

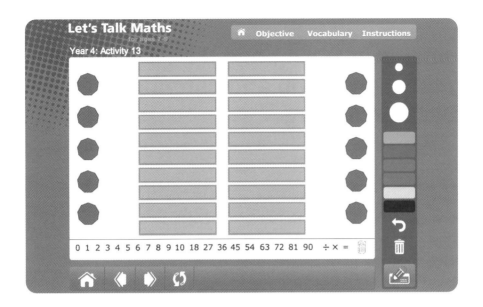

Discuss the nonagons – note that 'nonagon' is not required vocabulary for Year 4 but 'polygon' is. However, the nonagons are relevant to this activity and provide an opportunity to enrich the pupils' mathematical vocabulary – they may also be interested to learn that a nonagenarian is a person aged in their nineties and a nonet is a piece of music for nine singers or instruments! Ask the children why we might look at nonagons when we are discussing the 9 times table – hopefully they will say that each nonagon has 9 sides and 9 vertices. Discuss the fact that 2 nonagons will have 18 vertices altogether.

Ask the children to take turns to record a part of the 9 times table. As with all of these activities, encourage each child to ask the questions clearly using the appropriate vocabulary. Once the 9 times table is complete ask the children to find the corresponding division facts and to record these alongside the table.

Appropriate vocabulary

pair	multiply	divide
equals	times	share
sign	explain	number sentence
write	record	the same number as
calculate	calculation	operation
answer	inverse	pattern
nonagon	corner	explain
vertex	vertices	polygon

Year 4 Activity 14

Solve problems involving numbers and measures, including time, choosing and carrying out appropriate calculations

Building on previous learning

Before starting this unit check that the children can already:

- [ ] derive and recall all addition and subtraction facts for each number to at least 20
- [ ] derive and recall sums and differences of multiples of 10
- [ ] derive and recall all number pairs that total 100
- [ ] use knowledge of number operations and corresponding inverses, including doubling and halving, to estimate and check calculations
- [ ] count on or back in ones, twos, fives and tens
- [ ] recognise multiples of five
- [ ] read time to the nearest five minutes

Learning objectives

- Solve problems involving numbers and measures, including time, choosing and carrying out appropriate calculations
- Read the time to the nearest minute on an analogue clock
- Calculate time intervals and find start or end times for a given time interval
- Interpret intervals and divisions on partially numbered scales and record readings accurately

Learning outcomes

The children will be able to:

- read the time to the nearest minute on an analogue clock
- solve problems involving calculation of time intervals
- interpret intervals and the divisions on a clock face and record the times accurately

Success criteria

Can the children…

- [ ] read the time to the nearest minute on an analogue clock?
- [ ] find the number of minutes after the hour and the corresponding number of minutes to the next hour?
- [ ] state the end time for a given time interval when a start time is provided?
- [ ] state the start time for a given time interval when an end time is provided?

How to use the material for discussion

It is suggested that this activity is repeated over several short sessions, each session showing progression from the previous one. Click on the clock face to show different times that can be used for discussions using appropriate vocabulary. Confident pupils will be able to find start or end times for a given time interval that crosses an o'clock time.

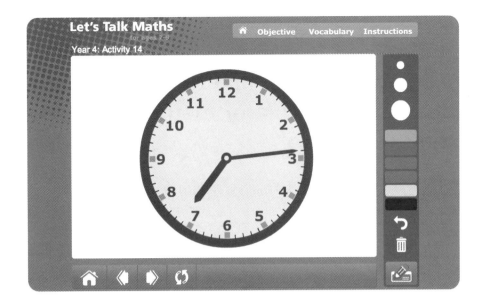

Many Year 4 pupils are not confident with reading the time. Revising time to the nearest five minutes should be the focus of the task the first time this activity is used. Encourage the pupils to notice the position of the hour hand – ie that it has moved part way between one hour and the next. Remind them that the numerals show the hours, with reference to the hour hand, and that they show every five minutes with reference to the minute hand.

The next time you use the activity ask the pupils to work out the exact times to the minute. Explain that they need to work out the time to the nearest five minutes then to add on or subtract minutes to find the exact time.

On another occasion you could ask the pupils to work out the time past the hour and to the next hour. As an example, the clock shown above could be discussed with questions such as: 'How many minutes past seven o'clock does the clock show?', 'How many minutes will it be until eight o'clock?'

Once you feel that the pupils are confident, ask questions such as: 'What time does the clock show?', 'What will the time be one hour and thirty minutes after that?', 'What would the time have been one hour and thirty minutes before that time?'

Appropriate vocabulary

count on	count back	multiple
clock	o'clock	quarter
half	hour	minutes
time	before	after
interval	start time	end time
hands	morning	afternoon
evening	midnight	midday
noon	night	day
am	pm	digital
analogue		

Solve one-step and two-step problems involving money, choosing and carrying out appropriate calculations, using calculator methods where appropriate

Building on previous learning

Before starting this unit check that the children can already:

- [ ] derive and recall all addition and subtraction facts for each number to at least 20
- [ ] derive and recall sums and differences of multiples of 10
- [ ] derive and recall all number pairs that total 100
- [ ] use knowledge of number operations and corresponding inverses, including doubling and halving, to estimate and check calculations

Learning objectives

- Solve problems involving adding in the context of money
- Solve problems involving subtracting in the context of money
- Solve one-step problems such as finding the total of or the difference between two amounts of money
- Solve two-step problems such as finding the total of two amounts of money then the change from £5 or £10 when this total is spent
- Refine and use efficient written methods to add and subtract £.p

Learning outcomes

The children will be able to:

- find total amounts to pay for two items
- find change from £5 when buying an item
- find differences in price between pairs of items
- find the total price of two items, then the change from £5 or £10

Success criteria

Can the children...

- [ ] add together two sums of money in pounds and pence to find the total cost of two priced items?
- [ ] find the change from £5 or £10 when buying some priced items?
- [ ] use the calculator efficiently and interpret the display correctly in the context of money?
- [ ] use appropriate vocabulary in relation to spending money and finding change?

How to use the material for discussion

Pupils will find total costs of pairs of priced items and make comparisons and find change from £1. With confident pupils you may wish to devise problems in relation to the priced items using all four number operations.

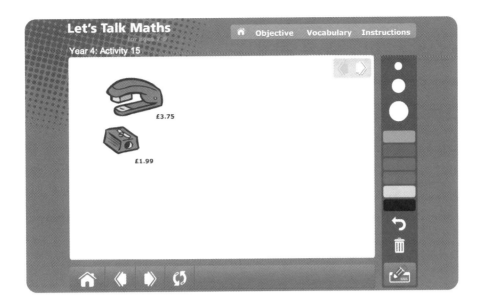

Upon opening the activity there will be two items displayed on the screen. Click on the top right hand arrow to display, one at a time, more items until all eight items are present. This gives opportunities to discuss each one in relation to £1, to £5 and to each other. Discuss the items asking questions such as:

- How much change would I have from five pounds if I bought the stapler?
- Which costs more, the stapler or the pencil sharpener? How can we work out how much more?
- How much would both items cost altogether? Is that more than or less than £5? How much more/less?

Now ask one of the pupils to think of some questions to ask the other pupils.

Finally you could ask an extended question: If you had £10 to spend which items would you choose? How much money would you have left over? (You may wish to let the children use the calculator and some paper to make jottings.)

Appropriate vocabulary

more	less	total
cost	altogether	difference
price	change	double
answer	explain	operation
pound	penny	pence
coin	add	subtract
multiply	double	calculate
note	calculator	

Interpret intervals and divisions on partially numbered scales and record readings accurately, where appropriate to the nearest tenth of a unit

Building on previous learning

Before starting this unit check that the children can already:

☐ use appropriate units to estimate, measure and record measurements to the nearest centimetre

☐ read, to the nearest division and half-division, scales that are numbered or partially numbered

Learning objectives

■ Interpret intervals and divisions on partially numbered scales and record readings accurately, where appropriate to the nearest tenth of a unit

■ Choose and use standard metric units and their abbreviations when estimating, measuring and recording length; know the meaning of 'centi' and 'milli' and use decimal notation to record measurements

Learning outcomes

The children will be able to:

■ use a picture of a ruler as an aid to developing their vocabulary in relation to measurement of length

■ measure to the nearest millimetre using a real ruler and record the measurement in centimetres and millimetres or in decimal notation in relation to centimetres

Success criteria

Can the children...

☐ use a ruler correctly to measure straight lines?

☐ use appropriate vocabulary in relation to measurement of length?

How to use the material for discussion

The task in this activity is to measure lines of different lengths with a ruler. It must be stressed to the pupils that this is a picture and is not of the correct size.
Discuss the different ways to state the lines' lengths, i.e. 3 centimetres, 4 millimetres or 3.4 centimetres.

Explain that the ruler shown on the screen is a picture of a ruler marked in centimetres – ensure that the pupils understand that it is only a picture and that centimetres are much smaller than those illustrated! Ask one of the children to drag one of the bold lines alongside the ruler to measure it. Watch carefully how the pupil places the line – some children will place the lines at the end of the ruler rather than at the 0 mark. Now discuss the length of the line, encouraging the children to state its length in centimetres and millimetres, then to state it in decimals only. Eg, for the line shown on this page: 4 centimetres, 6 millimetres; 4.6 centimetres.

Now ask one of the children to become the leader of the discussion. Measure the remaining lines.

It is essential that you continue this work with real rulers. Encourage the children to measure random straight lines that you have prepared for them. They could estimate the lengths to the nearest centimetre before measuring them accurately.

Appropriate vocabulary

ruler	zero	standard unit
metre	centimetre	millimetre
measure	accurate	length
measuring tape	metric unit	estimate
approximate		

Draw rectangles and measure and calculate their perimeters; find the area of rectilinear shapes drawn on a square grid by counting squares

Building on previous learning

Before starting this unit check that the children can already:

☐ use appropriate units to estimate, measure and record measurements to the nearest centimetre

☐ read, to the nearest division and half-division, scales that are numbered or partially numbered

Learning objectives

■ Draw rectangles and measure and calculate their perimeters

■ Find the area of rectilinear shapes drawn on a square grid by counting squares

Learning outcomes

The children will be able to:

■ use a picture of rectangles on a grid as an aid to developing their vocabulary in relation to measurement of perimeter and area

■ draw rectangles and find their perimeters

■ find the area of rectangles by counting squares

Success criteria

Can the children...

☐ find perimeters of rectangles by measuring and calculating?

☐ find areas of rectangles by counting squares?

☐ use appropriate vocabulary in relation to perimeter and area?

How to use the material for discussion

A grid of squares with four shaded rectangles is displayed. Pupils will be able to find the perimeters of the rectangles shown by adding the lengths of the sides. They will be able to find the areas by counting squares.

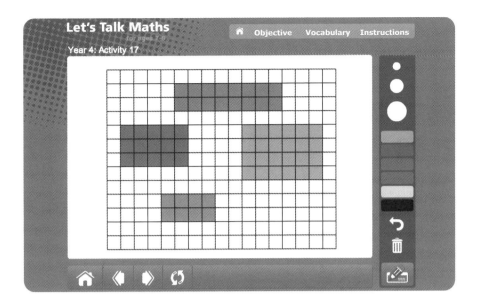

Explain that the grid shown on the screen is a picture of a grid marked in square centimetres – ensure that the pupils understand that it is only a picture and that square centimetres are much smaller than those illustrated! Explain that the distance around a shape is called its perimeter – you may wish to mention that the fence around the school could be described as the perimeter fence. Calculate the perimeter of one of the rectangles.

Now ask one of the children to become the leader of the discussion in relation to a different rectangle.

Following the discussion ask the children to draw some rectangles and to measure and calculate their perimeters.

On a different occasion you can use the same material to discuss area, pointing out that area is measured in square centimetres.

Appropriate vocabulary

perimeter	area	centimetre
square centimetre	grid	rectangle
length	distance	ruler
measure	measurement	

Identify pairs of fractions that total 1

Building on previous learning

Before starting this unit check that the children can already:

☐ read proper fractions

☐ interpret the denominator as parts of a whole

☐ interpret the numerator as the number of parts

Learning objectives

- Revise reading proper fractions
- Revise interpreting the denominator as parts of a whole
- Revise interpreting the numerator as the number of parts
- Identify pairs of fractions that total 1

Learning outcomes

The children will be able to:

- read fractions quickly and confidently
- complete addition and subtraction sentences involving fractions that total 1

Success criteria

Can the children...

☐ read fractions quickly and confidently?

☐ find fraction pairs that total 1?

☐ use appropriate vocabulary to discuss the fractions?

How to use the material for discussion

Before working on the presentation, take the opportunity to discuss real items that can be cut into parts, eg pizzas, cakes, etc. Encourage the children to make use of the diagrams so that they can observe the pairs of fraction that total 1 – ensure that they understand that the circle represents a 'whole', ie 1.

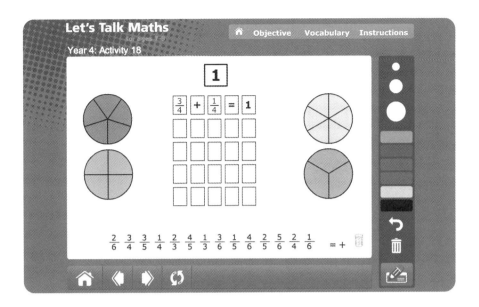

The activity consists of the teacher, or a pupil playing the role of leader, asking pupils to create addition sentences for fractions that total 1. They can refer to the appropriate fraction diagram to help answer the question. The appropriate fractions should be dragged from the bottom of the screen into the boxes provided. The leader should now ask other pupils to help them to complete addition sentences that total 1 with other appropriate fractions. Then another child could take the role of leader.

Appropriate vocabulary

fraction	part	equal parts
one whole	parts of a whole	number of parts
one half	one quarter	three quarters
one sixth	five sixths	one fifth
two fifths	three fifths	four fifths
one tenth	one third	three tenths
two thirds	one eighth	seven tenths
three eighths	nine tenths	five eighths
seven eighths	total	

Use the eight points of the compass to describe direction

Building on previous learning

Before starting this unit check that the children can already:

☐ read proper fractions

☐ interpret the denominator as parts of a whole

☐ interpret the numerator as the number of parts

Learning objectives

■ Use the eight points of the compass to describe direction

■ Know that angles are measured in degrees and that one whole turn is 360°

Learning outcomes

The children will be able to:

■ identify the eight points of the compass on a compass rose

■ describe directions after making turns through a specified number of right angles clockwise or anticlockwise

■ describe directions after making turns through a specified number of degrees clockwise or anticlockwise

Success criteria

Can the children...

☐ label a compass rose correctly with the eight compass directions?

☐ use appropriate vocabulary to discuss rotations?

How to use the material for discussion

In this activity the children label a compass rose appropriately with the names of the eight points. This can then be used as a focus for discussion of measurement in degrees.

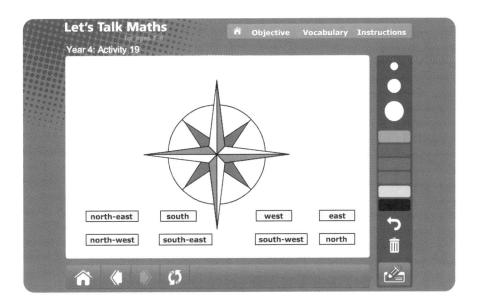

Ask a child to come to the screen and to drag a word to the correct place on the compass. That child should then choose another child to place another word in the correct place, etc. Once the compass is correctly labelled ask the children questions such as:

- If I am facing north and I turn through one right angle clockwise, in what direction will I be facing?

- If I am facing north and I turn through two right angles anticlockwise, in what direction will I be facing?

Now ask the children to make up questions for each other using the appropriate vocabulary.

When you feel that the children are confident you could ask them questions regarding rotations through angles specified in terms of degrees:

- If I am facing west and I turn through 90° clockwise, in what direction will I be facing?

- If I am facing south-east and I turn through 180° clockwise, in what direction will I be facing?

- What if I had turned 180° anticlockwise?

You may also like to use angles of 360° and 45°.

Appropriate vocabulary

north	south	east
west	north-west	north-east
south-west	south-east	compass
position	direction	point
clockwise	anticlockwise	right angle
rotation	degrees	

Published 2009 by A & C Black Publishers Limited
36 Soho Square, London W1D 3QY
www.acblack.com

ISBN 9781408111147

Copyright © A & C Black Publishers Limited
Written by Andrew Brodie
Page layout by Bob Vickers

A CIP record for this publication is available from the British Library.

Printed in Great Britain by Martins the Printers, Berwick-upon-Tweed.

This book is produced using paper that is made from wood grown in
managed, sustainable forests. It is natural, renewable and recyclable.
The logging and manufacturing processes conform to the environmental
regulations of the country of origin.

To see our full range of titles visit www.acblack.com